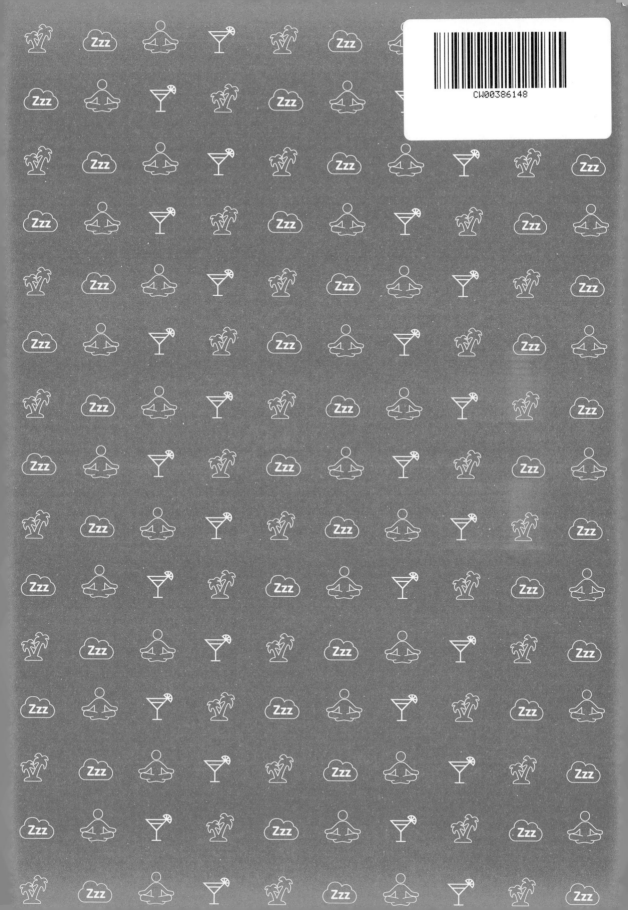

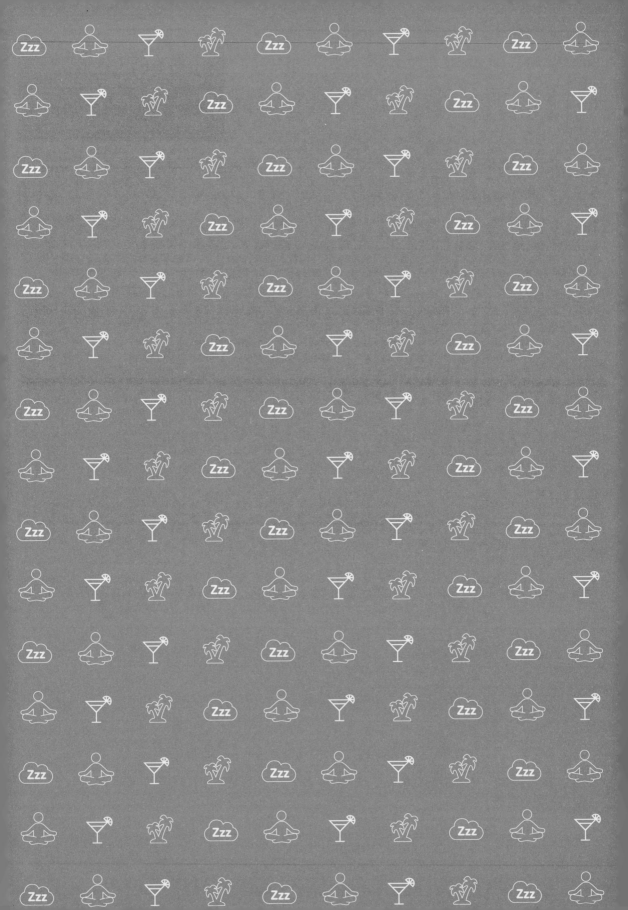

I NEED SOME SERIOUS
ME TIME

KNOCK KNOCK®
VENICE, CALIFORNIA

Created, published, and distributed by Knock Knock
1635 Electric Ave.
Venice, CA 90291
knockknockstuff.com
Knock Knock is a registered trademark of Knock Knock LLC
Inner-Truth is a trademark of Knock Knock LLC

ISBN: 978-160106991-7
UPC: 825703-50090-5

10 9 8 7 6 5 4 3 2 1

IF YOU NEED
ME, I'LL BE SOMEWHERE
ELSE. SOMEWHERE ELSE TOTALLY BY MYSELF.
SOMEWHERE ELSE FAR, FAR AWAY AND VERY

quiet. In other words, please leave me alone for a while. Okay? When Henry David Thoreau needed some "me time," he packed up and went to live simply in the woods for two years. When Wendell Berry felt "despair for the world" he would "go and lie down where the wood drake rests in his beauty on the water, and the great heron feeds" to "come into the peace of wild things."

When you've got too many texts, too many deadlines, too many noisy children, or just TOO MUCH, it's tempting to follow Henry and Wendell's leads and disappear for a spell. But who's got that kind of time? And how far would you have to drive to find the wood drake's resting spot? But a little quiet, a little peace—your very own emotional Walden Pond? That shouldn't be so hard to find, right?

In a *New York Times* column, essayist Tim Kreider opined, "Idleness is not just a vacation, an indulgence or a vice; it is as indispensable to the brain as vitamin D is to the body, and deprived of it we suffer a mental affliction as disfiguring as rickets." He's absolutely right. "Me time" is essential: to maintain your creative spark and your mental energy, to solve problems, to reduce stress, and to recharge.

According to *Scientific American*, "Downtime replenishes the brain's stores of attention and motivation, encourages productivity and creativity, and is essential to both achieve our highest levels of performance and simply form stable memories in everyday life." Even *Forbes,* which you might think would take a "work, work, work" point of view, asserts, "If we don't allow ourselves periods of uninterrupted, freely associated thought then personal growth, insight and creativity are less likely to emerge."

Now that you're able to make a case for more "me time," how do you actually make it happen? There are plenty of big ways and little ways to get the peace you need. *Science Magazine* suggests "work-free weekends, post-lunch catnaps, days off, vacations from technology, no-work evenings, and regular 10-minute work breaks." Other ideas: create a daily teatime, work on art, play an instrument, take a walk, meditate, hide in the bathroom (how did people find alone time before bathrooms?), stare out the window, daydream.

Or…write in a journal, like the one you happen to have in your hands! You'll reap the benefits of "me time" as well as those of journaling, which are (unsurprisingly) quite similar.

As noted self-help guru Deepak Chopra claims, "Journaling is one of the most powerful tools we have to transform our lives." According to a widely cited study by James W. Pennebaker and Janel D. Seagal, "Writing about important personal experiences in an emotional way…brings about improvements in mental and physical health." Proven benefits include better stress management, strengthened immune systems, fewer doctor visits, and improvement in chronic illnesses such as asthma.

It's not entirely clear how journaling accomplishes all this. Catharsis is involved, but many also point to the value of organizing experiences into a cohesive narrative. According to *Newsweek,* some experts believe that journaling "forces us to transform the ruminations cluttering our minds into coherent stories." In many ways, journaling enables us to see beyond the present moment to the future we want to create.

Keep in mind that it's also a process, a habit you can work on until it's second nature. Specialists agree that in order to reap the benefits of journaling you have to stick with it, quasi-daily, for as little as five minutes at a time (though at least fifteen minutes is best), even on the days when you can barely manage any "me time." Finding regular writing times and comfortable locations can help with consistency.

What should you write about? Write about moments when you felt most at peace and how you got there. Strategize how you'll get your "me time" in the future. Write about your frustrations and the things that are coming at you too quickly. Write about the things in your life that are actually really good. Fantasize about your perfect personal Walden Pond. Write whatever comes, and don't criticize it; journaling is a means of self-reflection, not a structured composition. In other words, spew. If you find yourself unable to think of anything to write, don't stress. Instead, use the quotes inside this journal as a jumping-off point for observations and explorations. And don't forget that the whole point is to achieve a little bit of quiet reflection, whatever that may be.

Finally, determine a home for your journal where you can find it easily, so you don't waste your precious time searching. Keep it where you like to hide: the bedroom, the tree house, your car, the basement, or the bath. Store some earplugs nearby as well. Or headphones, the gigantic noise-canceling kind.

Many of our most important moments of insight or creativity come in periods of sleep, relaxation, or daydreaming, aka "me time." That's when our brains get a chance to clear away the chaos and really get to work. Newton came to understand gravity sitting under a tree in his garden, when an apple dropped on him. Archimedes was taking a bath when he realized how to determine the volume of an item by the amount of water it displaces. Paul McCartney composed "Yesterday" in his sleep. Last week, you had that great redecorating idea in the shower. Keep seeking out "me time," making it a priority every day. You never know when something amazing might drop out of the sky and conk you on the head.

Everybody should be quiet near a little stream and listen.

RUTH KRAUSS

DATE

WHY I NEED ME TIME TODAY:

_____

_____

_____

_____

_____

_____

_____

_____

_____

_____

_____

_____

_____

_____

_____

_____

_____

_____

_____

_____

_____

_____

_____

_____

_____

_____

_____

_____

WHAT I'D RATHER BE DOING (ALL BY MYSELF AND TOTALLY ALONE):

I'd be quite happy if I spent Saturday night to Monday morning alone in my apartment. That's how I refuel.

AUDREY HEPBURN

DATE		

WHY I NEED ME TIME TODAY:

_____

_____

_____

_____

_____

_____

_____

_____

_____

_____

_____

_____

_____

_____

_____

_____

_____

_____

_____

_____

_____

_____

_____

_____

_____

_____

_____

_____

WHAT I'D RATHER BE DOING (ALL BY MYSELF AND TOTALLY ALONE):

How much better is silence;
the coffee-cup, the table. How
much better to sit by myself like
the solitary sea-bird that opens
its wings on the stake.

VIRGINIA WOOLF

WHY I NEED ME TIME TODAY:

_____

_____

_____

_____

_____

_____

_____

_____

_____

_____

_____

_____

_____

_____

_____

_____

_____

_____

_____

_____

_____

_____

_____

_____

_____

_____

_____

_____

_____

WHAT I'D RATHER BE DOING (ALL BY MYSELF AND TOTALLY ALONE):

My imagination functions much better when I don't have to speak with people.

PATRICIA HIGHSMITH

DATE		

WHY I NEED ME TIME TODAY:

_____

_____

_____

_____

_____

_____

_____

_____

_____

_____

_____

_____

_____

_____

_____

_____

_____

_____

_____

_____

_____

_____

_____

_____

_____

_____

_____

_____

_____

WHAT I'D RATHER BE DOING (ALL BY MYSELF AND TOTALLY ALONE):

At the end of the day I play ostrich. I take a glass of beer or wine or a pill and go to sleep to have energy for the next day.

ANAÏS NIN

DATE		

WHY I NEED ME TIME TODAY:

_____
_____
_____
_____
_____
_____
_____
_____
_____
_____
_____
_____
_____
_____
_____
_____
_____
_____
_____
_____
_____
_____
_____
_____
_____
_____
_____

WHAT I'D RATHER BE DOING (ALL BY MYSELF AND TOTALLY ALONE):

Often we can help each other most by leaving each other alone; at other times we need the hand-grasp and the word of cheer.

ELBERT HUBBARD

DATE		

WHY I NEED ME TIME TODAY:

_____

_____

_____

_____

_____

_____

_____

_____

_____

_____

_____

_____

_____

_____

_____

_____

_____

_____

_____

_____

_____

_____

_____

_____

_____

_____

WHAT I'D RATHER BE DOING (ALL BY MYSELF AND TOTALLY ALONE):

Life moves pretty fast. If you don't stop and look around once in a while, you could miss it.

JOHN HUGHES

WHY I NEED ME TIME TODAY:

_____
_____
_____
_____
_____
_____
_____
_____
_____
_____
_____
_____
_____
_____
_____
_____
_____
_____
_____
_____
_____
_____
_____
_____
_____
_____

WHAT I'D RATHER BE DOING (ALL BY MYSELF AND TOTALLY ALONE):

Besides the noble art of getting things done,
there is a nobler art of leaving things undone.

LIN YUTANG

DATE		

WHY I NEED ME TIME TODAY:

_____

_____

_____

_____

_____

_____

_____

_____

_____

_____

_____

_____

_____

_____

_____

_____

_____

_____

_____

_____

_____

_____

_____

_____

_____

_____

_____

_____

_____

WHAT I'D RATHER BE DOING (ALL BY MYSELF AND TOTALLY ALONE):

I would rather sit on a pumpkin and have it all to myself than be crowded on a velvet cushion.

HENRY DAVID THOREAU

DATE		

WHY I NEED ME TIME TODAY:

_____

_____

_____

_____

_____

_____

_____

_____

_____

_____

_____

_____

_____

_____

_____

_____

_____

_____

_____

_____

_____

_____

_____

_____

_____

WHAT I'D RATHER BE DOING (ALL BY MYSELF AND TOTALLY ALONE):

In order to understand the world, one has to turn away from it on occasion.

ALBERT CAMUS

	DATE	

WHY I NEED ME TIME TODAY:

_____

_____

_____

_____

_____

_____

_____

_____

_____

_____

_____

_____

_____

_____

_____

_____

_____

_____

_____

_____

_____

_____

_____

_____

_____

WHAT I'D RATHER BE DOING (ALL BY MYSELF AND TOTALLY ALONE):

I learned that solitude has its
own very strange beauty to it.

LIV TYLER

	DATE	

WHY I NEED ME TIME TODAY:

_____

_____

_____

_____

_____

_____

_____

_____

_____

_____

_____

_____

_____

_____

_____

_____

_____

_____

_____

_____

_____

_____

_____

_____

_____

_____

_____

_____

_____

WHAT I'D RATHER BE DOING (ALL BY MYSELF AND TOTALLY ALONE):

I'll read my books
and I'll drink the hot
coffee and I'll listen to
the music, and I'll bolt
the door.

J. D. SALINGER

	DATE	

WHY I NEED ME TIME TODAY:

_____

_____

_____

_____

_____

_____

_____

_____

_____

_____

_____

_____

_____

_____

_____

_____

_____

_____

_____

_____

_____

_____

_____

_____

WHAT I'D RATHER BE DOING (ALL BY MYSELF AND TOTALLY ALONE):

The vampires in your life can't be cured.
Your best bet is to stay away from them.

—————

AUSTIN KLEON

WHY I NEED ME TIME TODAY:

WHAT I'D RATHER BE DOING (ALL BY MYSELF AND TOTALLY ALONE):

But what one writer can make in the solitude of one room is something no power can easily destroy.

SALMAN RUSHDIE

DATE		

WHY I NEED ME TIME TODAY:

_____

_____

_____

_____

_____

_____

_____

_____

_____

_____

_____

_____

_____

_____

_____

_____

_____

_____

_____

_____

_____

_____

_____

_____

_____

_____

_____

_____

_____

_____

_____

_____

WHAT I'D RATHER BE DOING (ALL BY MYSELF AND TOTALLY ALONE):

I will be calm. I will be mistress of myself.

JANE AUSTEN

DATE

WHY I NEED ME TIME TODAY:

_____

_____

_____

_____

_____

_____

_____

_____

_____

_____

_____

_____

_____

_____

_____

_____

_____

_____

_____

_____

_____

_____

_____

_____

_____

WHAT I'D RATHER BE DOING (ALL BY MYSELF AND TOTALLY ALONE):

Recharge for as long as you need. Lean up against a tree and take a break from the other bears.

———

AMY SCHUMER

DATE		

WHY I NEED ME TIME TODAY:

_____

_____

_____

_____

_____

_____

_____

_____

_____

_____

_____

_____

_____

_____

_____

_____

_____

_____

_____

_____

_____

_____

_____

_____

_____

_____

_____

_____

_____

_____

_____

_____

WHAT I'D RATHER BE DOING (ALL BY MYSELF AND TOTALLY ALONE):

Then, I turned around and walked to my room and closed my door and put my head under my pillow and let the quiet put things where they are supposed to be.

STEPHEN CHBOSKY

	DATE	

WHY I NEED ME TIME TODAY:

_____

_____

_____

_____

_____

_____

_____

_____

_____

_____

_____

_____

_____

_____

_____

_____

_____

_____

_____

_____

_____

_____

_____

_____

_____

_____

_____

_____

_____

_____

_____

_____

_____

WHAT I'D RATHER BE DOING (ALL BY MYSELF AND TOTALLY ALONE):

I never said, "I want to be alone." I only said, "I want to be *let* alone!" There is all the difference.

GRETA GARBO

	DATE	

WHY I NEED ME TIME TODAY:

_____

_____

_____

_____

_____

_____

_____

_____

_____

_____

_____

_____

_____

_____

_____

_____

_____

_____

_____

_____

_____

_____

_____

_____

_____

_____

_____

_____

_____

WHAT I'D RATHER BE DOING (ALL BY MYSELF AND TOTALLY ALONE):

I'm someone who just likes being in my cave and thinking up weird stuff.

COLSON WHITEHEAD

WHY I NEED ME TIME TODAY:

_____

_____

_____

_____

_____

_____

_____

_____

_____

_____

_____

_____

_____

_____

_____

_____

_____

_____

_____

_____

_____

_____

_____

_____

_____

_____

_____

WHAT I'D RATHER BE DOING (ALL BY MYSELF AND TOTALLY ALONE):

Sometimes the most important thing in a whole day is the rest we take between two deep breaths.

ETTY HILLESUM

WHY I NEED ME TIME TODAY:

_____

_____

_____

_____

_____

_____

_____

_____

_____

_____

_____

_____

_____

_____

_____

_____

_____

_____

_____

_____

_____

_____

_____

_____

_____

WHAT I'D RATHER BE DOING (ALL BY MYSELF AND TOTALLY ALONE):

The secret of a good old age is simply an honorable pact with solitude.

GABRIEL GARCÍA MÁRQUEZ

DATE		

WHY I NEED ME TIME TODAY:

_____

_____

_____

_____

_____

_____

_____

_____

_____

_____

_____

_____

_____

_____

_____

_____

_____

_____

_____

_____

_____

_____

_____

_____

_____

WHAT I'D RATHER BE DOING (ALL BY MYSELF AND TOTALLY ALONE):

In terms of, like, instant relief, canceling plans is like heroin.

———————

JOHN MULANEY

	DATE	

WHY I NEED ME TIME TODAY:

_____

_____

_____

_____

_____

_____

_____

_____

_____

_____

_____

_____

_____

_____

_____

_____

_____

_____

_____

_____

_____

_____

_____

WHAT I'D RATHER BE DOING (ALL BY MYSELF AND TOTALLY ALONE):

O misery, misery, mumble and moan!

Someone invented the telephone,

And interrupted a nation's slumbers,

Ringing wrong but similar numbers.

OGDEN NASH

	DATE	

WHY I NEED ME TIME TODAY:

_____
_____
_____
_____
_____
_____
_____
_____
_____
_____
_____
_____
_____
_____
_____
_____
_____
_____
_____
_____
_____
_____
_____
_____
_____
_____
_____
_____
_____

WHAT I'D RATHER BE DOING (ALL BY MYSELF AND TOTALLY ALONE):

Tired with nothing, tired with everything, with the world's weight he had never chosen to bear.

F. SCOTT FITZGERALD

DATE		

WHY I NEED ME TIME TODAY:

_____
_____
_____
_____
_____
_____
_____
_____
_____
_____
_____
_____
_____
_____
_____
_____
_____
_____
_____
_____
_____
_____
_____
_____
_____
_____

WHAT I'D RATHER BE DOING (ALL BY MYSELF AND TOTALLY ALONE):

Seven minutes of another person's company was enough to give her a headache.

STIEG LARSSON

WHY I NEED ME TIME TODAY:

_____

_____

_____

_____

_____

_____

_____

_____

_____

_____

_____

_____

_____

_____

_____

_____

_____

_____

_____

_____

_____

_____

_____

_____

_____

WHAT I'D RATHER BE DOING (ALL BY MYSELF AND TOTALLY ALONE):

So on any given Sunday, you will find me alone. Filling myself up. Cherishing life and loving every solitary moment.

———————

OPRAH WINFREY

WHY I NEED ME TIME TODAY:

_____

_____

_____

_____

_____

_____

_____

_____

_____

_____

_____

_____

_____

_____

_____

_____

_____

_____

_____

_____

_____

_____

_____

_____

_____

_____

WHAT I'D RATHER BE DOING (ALL BY MYSELF AND TOTALLY ALONE):

A Soul admitted to Itself:

Finite Infinity.

EMILY DICKINSON

WHY I NEED ME TIME TODAY:

_____

_____

_____

_____

_____

_____

_____

_____

_____

_____

_____

_____

_____

_____

_____

_____

_____

_____

_____

_____

_____

_____

_____

_____

_____

_____

WHAT I'D RATHER BE DOING (ALL BY MYSELF AND TOTALLY ALONE):

A poet is a nightingale, who sits in darkness and sings to cheer its own solitude with sweet sounds.

PERCY BYSSHE SHELLEY

DATE		

WHY I NEED ME TIME TODAY:

_____

_____

_____

_____

_____

_____

_____

_____

_____

_____

_____

_____

_____

_____

_____

_____

_____

_____

_____

_____

_____

_____

_____

_____

_____

_____

_____

_____

WHAT I'D RATHER BE DOING (ALL BY MYSELF AND TOTALLY ALONE):

When I am composed I feel no need of affiliating myself with anybody. There is a lot of the cat in me, and cats are not joiners.

E. B. WHITE

DATE

WHY I NEED ME TIME TODAY:

_____

_____

_____

_____

_____

_____

_____

_____

_____

_____

_____

_____

_____

_____

_____

_____

_____

_____

_____

_____

_____

_____

_____

_____

_____

_____

_____

WHAT I'D RATHER BE DOING (ALL BY MYSELF AND TOTALLY ALONE):

When I bought a house, the first thing I did was to plant trees. I could not conceal myself enough. Set a hedge here, set pines there, trees & trees, set evergreens, above all, for they will keep my secret all year round.

RALPH WALDO EMERSON

DATE		

WHY I NEED ME TIME TODAY:

_____

_____

_____

_____

_____

_____

_____

_____

_____

_____

_____

_____

_____

_____

_____

_____

_____

_____

_____

_____

_____

_____

_____

_____

_____

_____

_____

_____

_____

_____

_____

WHAT I'D RATHER BE DOING (ALL BY MYSELF AND TOTALLY ALONE):

Here, in my solitude,
I have the feeling that
I contain too much
humanity.

INGMAR BERGMAN

DATE		

WHY I NEED ME TIME TODAY:

_____

_____

_____

_____

_____

_____

_____

_____

_____

_____

_____

_____

_____

_____

_____

_____

_____

_____

_____

_____

_____

_____

_____

_____

_____

_____

_____

_____

WHAT I'D RATHER BE DOING (ALL BY MYSELF AND TOTALLY ALONE):

For a second I was almost jealous of the clouds.

KAMILA SHAMSIE

DATE		

WHY I NEED ME TIME TODAY:

_____

_____

_____

_____

_____

_____

_____

_____

_____

_____

_____

_____

_____

_____

_____

_____

_____

_____

_____

_____

_____

_____

_____

_____

_____

_____

WHAT I'D RATHER BE DOING (ALL BY MYSELF AND TOTALLY ALONE):

Silence is more important than ever, as life today is full of noise. We speak a lot about environmental pollution but not enough about noise pollution.

ANDREA BOCELLI

	DATE	

WHY I NEED ME TIME TODAY:

_____

_____

_____

_____

_____

_____

_____

_____

_____

_____

_____

_____

_____

_____

_____

_____

_____

_____

_____

_____

_____

_____

_____

_____

_____

_____

_____

_____

_____

_____

_____

_____

WHAT I'D RATHER BE DOING (ALL BY MYSELF AND TOTALLY ALONE):

Literature is the pleasantest way of ignoring life.

FERNANDO PESSOA

WHY I NEED ME TIME TODAY:

_____

_____

_____

_____

_____

_____

_____

_____

_____

_____

_____

_____

_____

_____

_____

_____

_____

_____

_____

_____

_____

_____

_____

_____

_____

WHAT I'D RATHER BE DOING (ALL BY MYSELF AND TOTALLY ALONE):

Solitude is different from loneliness, and it doesn't have to be a lonely kind of thing.

FRED ROGERS

DATE

WHY I NEED ME TIME TODAY:

_____

_____

_____

_____

_____

_____

_____

_____

_____

_____

_____

_____

_____

_____

_____

_____

_____

_____

_____

_____

_____

_____

_____

_____

_____

_____

_____

_____

_____

WHAT I'D RATHER BE DOING (ALL BY MYSELF AND TOTALLY ALONE):

I'm happier being outside the flow.

NICHOLSON BAKER

DATE		

WHY I NEED ME TIME TODAY:

_____

_____

_____

_____

_____

_____

_____

_____

_____

_____

_____

_____

_____

_____

_____

_____

_____

_____

_____

_____

_____

_____

_____

_____

_____

_____

_____

WHAT I'D RATHER BE DOING (ALL BY MYSELF AND TOTALLY ALONE):

Realize deeply that the present moment is all you ever have.

ECKHART TOLLE

DATE		

WHY I NEED ME TIME TODAY:

_____

_____

_____

_____

_____

_____

_____

_____

_____

_____

_____

_____

_____

_____

_____

_____

_____

_____

_____

_____

_____

_____

_____

_____

_____

_____

_____

_____

_____

_____

_____

WHAT I'D RATHER BE DOING (ALL BY MYSELF AND TOTALLY ALONE):

I have to tell you I *love* living in a world without clocks. The shackles are gone. I'm a puppy unleashed in a meadow of time.

JERRY SPINELLI

DATE		

WHY I NEED ME TIME TODAY:

_____

_____

_____

_____

_____

_____

_____

_____

_____

_____

_____

_____

_____

_____

_____

_____

_____

_____

_____

_____

_____

_____

_____

_____

_____

_____

WHAT I'D RATHER BE DOING (ALL BY MYSELF AND TOTALLY ALONE):

The secret of contentment...lay in ignoring many things completely.

MARK HADDON

DATE

WHY I NEED ME TIME TODAY:

_____

_____

_____

_____

_____

_____

_____

_____

_____

_____

_____

_____

_____

_____

_____

_____

_____

_____

_____

_____

_____

_____

WHAT I'D RATHER BE DOING (ALL BY MYSELF AND TOTALLY ALONE):

Now I no longer wish to be loved, beautiful, happy or successful. I want one thing and one thing only—to be left alone.

JEAN RHYS

	DATE	

WHY I NEED ME TIME TODAY:

_____

_____

_____

_____

_____

_____

_____

_____

_____

_____

_____

_____

_____

_____

_____

_____

_____

_____

_____

_____

_____

_____

_____

_____

WHAT I'D RATHER BE DOING (ALL BY MYSELF AND TOTALLY ALONE):

My own formula is roughly two hours alone for every hour of socializing.

JONATHAN RAUCH

	DATE	

WHY I NEED ME TIME TODAY:

_____

_____

_____

_____

_____

_____

_____

_____

_____

_____

_____

_____

_____

_____

_____

_____

_____

_____

_____

_____

_____

_____

_____

WHAT I'D RATHER BE DOING (ALL BY MYSELF AND TOTALLY ALONE):

Alone had always felt like an actual place to me, as if it weren't a state of being, but rather a room where I could retreat to be who I really was.

CHERYL STRAYED

DATE		

WHY I NEED ME TIME TODAY:

_____

_____

_____

_____

_____

_____

_____

_____

_____

_____

_____

_____

_____

_____

_____

_____

_____

_____

_____

_____

_____

_____

_____

_____

_____

_____

_____

WHAT I'D RATHER BE DOING (ALL BY MYSELF AND TOTALLY ALONE):

I don't think we spend enough time in silence, just realizing what's floating around in our noggin.

SANDRA BULLOCK

DATE

WHY I NEED ME TIME TODAY:

_____

_____

_____

_____

_____

_____

_____

_____

_____

_____

_____

_____

_____

_____

_____

_____

_____

_____

_____

_____

_____

_____

_____

_____

_____

WHAT I'D RATHER BE DOING (ALL BY MYSELF AND TOTALLY ALONE):

Climb the mountains and get their good tidings. Nature's peace will flow into you as sunshine flows into trees. The winds will blow their own freshness into you, and the storms their energy, while cares will drop off like autumn leaves.

JOHN MUIR

DATE		

WHY I NEED ME TIME TODAY:

_____

_____

_____

_____

_____

_____

_____

_____

_____

_____

_____

_____

_____

_____

_____

_____

_____

_____

_____

_____

_____

_____

_____

_____

_____

_____

WHAT I'D RATHER BE DOING (ALL BY MYSELF AND TOTALLY ALONE):

For solitude sometimes
is best society,

And short retirement
urges sweet return.

JOHN MILTON

DATE		

WHY I NEED ME TIME TODAY:

_____

_____

_____

_____

_____

_____

_____

_____

_____

_____

_____

_____

_____

_____

_____

_____

_____

_____

_____

_____

_____

_____

_____

_____

_____

_____

WHAT I'D RATHER BE DOING (ALL BY MYSELF AND TOTALLY ALONE):

I would rather be excused
from your banquet of happiness.

SAMUEL TAYLOR COLERIDGE

DATE	

WHY I NEED ME TIME TODAY:

_____

_____

_____

_____

_____

_____

_____

_____

_____

_____

_____

_____

_____

_____

_____

_____

_____

_____

_____

_____

_____

_____

_____

_____

_____

_____

_____

_____

_____

_____

_____

WHAT I'D RATHER BE DOING (ALL BY MYSELF AND TOTALLY ALONE):

Certain springs are tapped only when we are alone.

ANNE MORROW LINDBERGH

DATE		

WHY I NEED ME TIME TODAY:

_____

_____

_____

_____

_____

_____

_____

_____

_____

_____

_____

_____

_____

_____

_____

_____

_____

_____

_____

_____

_____

_____

_____

_____

_____

_____

WHAT I'D RATHER BE DOING (ALL BY MYSELF AND TOTALLY ALONE):

Turn off your mind, relax, and float downstream.

JOHN LENNON

DATE		

WHY I NEED ME TIME TODAY:

_____

_____

_____

_____

_____

_____

_____

_____

_____

_____

_____

_____

_____

_____

_____

_____

_____

_____

_____

_____

_____

_____

_____

_____

_____

_____

_____

_____

WHAT I'D RATHER BE DOING (ALL BY MYSELF AND TOTALLY ALONE):

Reading was my escape and my comfort, my consolation, my stimulant of choice: reading for the pure pleasure of it, for the beautiful stillness that surrounds you when you hear an author's words reverberating in your head.

PAUL AUSTER

WHY I NEED ME TIME TODAY:

_____

_____

_____

_____

_____

_____

_____

_____

_____

_____

_____

_____

_____

_____

_____

_____

_____

_____

_____

_____

_____

_____

_____

_____

WHAT I'D RATHER BE DOING (ALL BY MYSELF AND TOTALLY ALONE):

Been waiting for the night to fall /

Now everything is bearable /

And here in the still /

All that you hear /

Is tranquility

	DATE	

WHY I NEED ME TIME TODAY:

_____

_____

_____

_____

_____

_____

_____

_____

_____

_____

_____

_____

_____

_____

_____

_____

_____

_____

_____

_____

_____

_____

_____

_____

_____

_____

_____

_____

_____

WHAT I'D RATHER BE DOING (ALL BY MYSELF AND TOTALLY ALONE):

What I always craved was solitude, because I think silence is refreshment for our souls.

NAOMI JUDD

DATE		

WHY I NEED ME TIME TODAY:

_____

_____

_____

_____

_____

_____

_____

_____

_____

_____

_____

_____

_____

_____

_____

_____

_____

_____

_____

_____

_____

_____

_____

_____

_____

_____

_____

_____

_____

WHAT I'D RATHER BE DOING (ALL BY MYSELF AND TOTALLY ALONE):

Silence is deep as Eternity;
speech is shallow as Time.

———

THOMAS CARLYLE

DATE		

WHY I NEED ME TIME TODAY:

_____

_____

_____

_____

_____

_____

_____

_____

_____

_____

_____

_____

_____

_____

_____

_____

_____

_____

_____

_____

_____

_____

_____

_____

_____

_____

_____

_____

WHAT I'D RATHER BE DOING (ALL BY MYSELF AND TOTALLY ALONE):

We have so much time and so little to do! No! Wait! Strike that! Reverse it! Thank you!

ROALD DAHL

DATE

WHY I NEED ME TIME TODAY:

_____

_____

_____

_____

_____

_____

_____

_____

_____

_____

_____

_____

_____

_____

_____

_____

_____

_____

_____

_____

_____

_____

_____

_____

_____

_____

_____

_____

_____

WHAT I'D RATHER BE DOING (ALL BY MYSELF AND TOTALLY ALONE):

His habit of reading isolated him: it became such a need that after being in company for some time he grew tired and restless.

WILLIAM SOMERSET MAUGHAM

WHY I NEED ME TIME TODAY:

_____

_____

_____

_____

_____

_____

_____

_____

_____

_____

_____

_____

_____

_____

_____

_____

_____

_____

_____

_____

_____

_____

_____

_____

_____

WHAT I'D RATHER BE DOING (ALL BY MYSELF AND TOTALLY ALONE):

Your mind will answer most questions if
you learn to relax and wait for the answer.

WILLIAM S. BURROUGHS

	DATE	

WHY I NEED ME TIME TODAY:

_____
_____
_____
_____
_____
_____
_____
_____
_____
_____
_____
_____
_____
_____
_____
_____
_____
_____
_____
_____
_____
_____
_____

WHAT I'D RATHER BE DOING (ALL BY MYSELF AND TOTALLY ALONE):

Chapter books were my salvation, in the same way as Jesus was for other kids.

ANNE LAMOTT

DATE		

WHY I NEED ME TIME TODAY:

_____
_____
_____
_____
_____
_____
_____
_____
_____
_____
_____
_____
_____
_____
_____
_____
_____
_____
_____
_____
_____
_____
_____
_____
_____
_____

WHAT I'D RATHER BE DOING (ALL BY MYSELF AND TOTALLY ALONE):

We live, in fact, in a world starved for solitude, silence, and privacy.

C. S. LEWIS

DATE		

WHY I NEED ME TIME TODAY:

_____

_____

_____

_____

_____

_____

_____

_____

_____

_____

_____

_____

_____

_____

_____

_____

_____

_____

_____

_____

_____

_____

_____

_____

_____

_____

_____

_____

WHAT I'D RATHER BE DOING (ALL BY MYSELF AND TOTALLY ALONE):

There must be some
way out of here, said
the joker to the thief /
There's too much
confusion, I can't get
no relief

BOB DYLAN

DATE		

WHY I NEED ME TIME TODAY:

_____

_____

_____

_____

_____

_____

_____

_____

_____

_____

_____

_____

_____

_____

_____

_____

_____

_____

_____

_____

_____

_____

_____

_____

_____

WHAT I'D RATHER BE DOING (ALL BY MYSELF AND TOTALLY ALONE):

This was my moment to look for
the kind of healing and peace that can
only come from solitude.

ELIZABETH GILBERT

WHY I NEED ME TIME TODAY:

_____

_____

_____

_____

_____

_____

_____

_____

_____

_____

_____

_____

_____

_____

_____

_____

_____

_____

_____

_____

_____

_____

_____

_____

_____

WHAT I'D RATHER BE DOING (ALL BY MYSELF AND TOTALLY ALONE):

The reason
to travel: there are
inner transitions we
can't properly cement
without a change of
locations.

ALAIN DE BOTTON

	DATE	

WHY I NEED ME TIME TODAY:

_____

_____

_____

_____

_____

_____

_____

_____

_____

_____

_____

_____

_____

_____

_____

_____

_____

_____

_____

_____

_____

_____

_____

WHAT I'D RATHER BE DOING (ALL BY MYSELF AND TOTALLY ALONE):

I cannot follow you where I will not go.

EDMOND JABÈS

DATE		

WHY I NEED ME TIME TODAY:

_____

_____

_____

_____

_____

_____

_____

_____

_____

_____

_____

_____

_____

_____

_____

_____

_____

_____

_____

_____

_____

_____

_____

_____

_____

WHAT I'D RATHER BE DOING (ALL BY MYSELF AND TOTALLY ALONE):

When from our better selves
  we have too long

Been parted by the hurrying
  world, and droop,

Sick of its business, of its
  pleasures tired,

How gracious, how benign,
  is Solitude.

WILLIAM WORDSWORTH

DATE

WHY I NEED ME TIME TODAY:

_____

_____

_____

_____

_____

_____

_____

_____

_____

_____

_____

_____

_____

_____

_____

_____

_____

_____

_____

_____

_____

_____

_____

WHAT I'D RATHER BE DOING (ALL BY MYSELF AND TOTALLY ALONE):

I am the Merry Recluse.

———

CAROLINE KNAPP

DATE	

WHY I NEED ME TIME TODAY:

_____

_____

_____

_____

_____

_____

_____

_____

_____

_____

_____

_____

_____

_____

_____

_____

_____

_____

_____

_____

_____

_____

_____

_____

_____

_____

_____

_____

WHAT I'D RATHER BE DOING (ALL BY MYSELF AND TOTALLY ALONE):

I'm not lonely, and I think that has a lot to do with what's on my bedside table rather than what's in my bed.

MICHELLE WILLIAMS

DATE		

WHY I NEED ME TIME TODAY:

_____

_____

_____

_____

_____

_____

_____

_____

_____

_____

_____

_____

_____

_____

_____

_____

_____

_____

_____

_____

_____

_____

_____

_____

WHAT I'D RATHER BE DOING (ALL BY MYSELF AND TOTALLY ALONE):

Idleness is an appendix to nobility.

ROBERT BURTON

DATE		

WHY I NEED ME TIME TODAY:

_____

_____

_____

_____

_____

_____

_____

_____

_____

_____

_____

_____

_____

_____

_____

_____

_____

_____

_____

_____

_____

_____

_____

WHAT I'D RATHER BE DOING (ALL BY MYSELF AND TOTALLY ALONE):

I need the sunshine and the paving stones of the streets without companions, without conversation, face to face with myself, with only the music of my heart for company.

HENRY MILLER

DATE		

WHY I NEED ME TIME TODAY:

_____

_____

_____

_____

_____

_____

_____

_____

_____

_____

_____

_____

_____

_____

_____

_____

_____

_____

_____

_____

_____

_____

_____

_____

WHAT I'D RATHER BE DOING (ALL BY MYSELF AND TOTALLY ALONE):

Certainly work is not always required of a man. There is such a thing as a sacred idleness, the cultivation of which is now fearfully neglected.

GEORGE MACDONALD

DATE		

WHY I NEED ME TIME TODAY:

_____

_____

_____

_____

_____

_____

_____

_____

_____

_____

_____

_____

_____

_____

_____

_____

_____

_____

_____

_____

_____

_____

_____

_____

_____

_____

_____

WHAT I'D RATHER BE DOING (ALL BY MYSELF AND TOTALLY ALONE):

Distracted from distraction by distraction.

———

T. S. ELIOT

WHY I NEED ME TIME TODAY:

_____

_____

_____

_____

_____

_____

_____

_____

_____

_____

_____

_____

_____

_____

_____

_____

_____

_____

_____

_____

_____

_____

_____

_____

_____

WHAT I'D RATHER BE DOING (ALL BY MYSELF AND TOTALLY ALONE):

I have not a desire but a need for solitude.

ROLAND BARTHES

DATE

WHY I NEED ME TIME TODAY:

WHAT I'D RATHER BE DOING (ALL BY MYSELF AND TOTALLY ALONE):

I feel like I could throw off sparks, or break a window—maybe rearrange all the furniture.

RAYMOND CARVER

DATE

WHY I NEED ME TIME TODAY:

_____
_____
_____
_____
_____
_____
_____
_____
_____
_____
_____
_____
_____
_____
_____
_____
_____
_____
_____
_____
_____
_____
_____
_____
_____

WHAT I'D RATHER BE DOING (ALL BY MYSELF AND TOTALLY ALONE):

No live organism
can continue for long
to exist sanely under
conditions of absolute
reality.

SHIRLEY JACKSON

WHY I NEED ME TIME TODAY:

_____

_____

_____

_____

_____

_____

_____

_____

_____

_____

_____

_____

_____

_____

_____

_____

_____

_____

_____

_____

_____

_____

_____

_____

_____

_____

WHAT I'D RATHER BE DOING (ALL BY MYSELF AND TOTALLY ALONE):

Perhaps the truth depends on a walk around the lake.

WALLACE STEVENS

DATE		

WHY I NEED ME TIME TODAY:

_____

_____

_____

_____

_____

_____

_____

_____

_____

_____

_____

_____

_____

_____

_____

_____

_____

_____

_____

_____

_____

_____

_____

WHAT I'D RATHER BE DOING (ALL BY MYSELF AND TOTALLY ALONE):

Sometimes I wonder how all those
who do not write, compose, or paint
can manage to escape the madness.

GRAHAM GREENE

	DATE	

WHY I NEED ME TIME TODAY:

_____

_____

_____

_____

_____

_____

_____

_____

_____

_____

_____

_____

_____

_____

_____

_____

_____

_____

_____

_____

_____

_____

_____

_____

_____

WHAT I'D RATHER BE DOING (ALL BY MYSELF AND TOTALLY ALONE):

Nothing can be
done without solitude.
I've created my own
solitude which nobody
suspects.

PABLO PICASSO

WHY I NEED ME TIME TODAY:

WHAT I'D RATHER BE DOING (ALL BY MYSELF AND TOTALLY ALONE):

Be a good steward of your gifts.
Protect your time. Feed your inner life.
Avoid too much noise. Read good books,
have good sentences in your ears.
Be by yourself as often as you can.

JANE KENYON

DATE

WHY I NEED ME TIME TODAY:

_____

_____

_____

_____

_____

_____

_____

_____

_____

_____

_____

_____

_____

_____

_____

_____

_____

_____

_____

_____

_____

_____

_____

_____

_____

WHAT I'D RATHER BE DOING (ALL BY MYSELF AND TOTALLY ALONE):

I just wanted to lie in the grass and look at the clouds.

JACK KEROUAC

DATE		

WHY I NEED ME TIME TODAY:

_____

_____

_____

_____

_____

_____

_____

_____

_____

_____

_____

_____

_____

_____

_____

_____

_____

_____

_____

_____

_____

_____

_____

WHAT I'D RATHER BE DOING (ALL BY MYSELF AND TOTALLY ALONE):

There is a time for many words and there is a time for sleep.

HOMER

DATE		

WHY I NEED ME TIME TODAY:

_____

_____

_____

_____

_____

_____

_____

_____

_____

_____

_____

_____

_____

_____

_____

_____

_____

_____

_____

_____

_____

_____

_____

WHAT I'D RATHER BE DOING (ALL BY MYSELF AND TOTALLY ALONE):

It's seriously you time.

———

KNOCK KNOCK